THE SEARCH

PARTICIPANT GUIDE

THE
SEARCH

TABLE OF CONTENTS

THE SEARCH

Scripture verses contained herein are from the English Standard Version of the Bible, Catholic Edition, published as *The Augustine Bible* by the Augustine Institute copyright © 2019. The Holy Bible, English Standard Version (ESV) copyright © 2001 by Crossway, a publishing ministry of Good News Publishers. Used by permission. All rights reserved. ESV Catholic Edition with Deuterocanonical Books copyright © 2017 by Crossway. ESV Catholic Edition Text: Used by permission. All rights reserved. The Deuterocanonical Books of the Apocrypha copyright © 2009 by Crossway.

Excerpts from the English translation of the *Catechism of the Catholic Church* for use in the United States of America copyright © 1994, United States Catholic Conference, Inc.—Libreria Editrice Vaticana. English translation of the *Catechism of the Catholic Church: Modifications from the Editio Typica* copyright © 1997, United States Conference of Catholic Bishops—Libreria Editrice Vaticana.

Writer: Sean Dalton

Graphic Design: based on the Augustine Studios design team (Justin Leddick, Kevin Mallory, and Steve Flanigan). Layout by 5 Stones Group, NFP

Film Series Production: Augustine Institute Studios

AUGUSTINE INSTITUTE

6160 South Syracuse Way, Suite 310
Greenwood Village, CO 80111
Information: 303-937-4420
AugustineInstitute.org
Formed.org

Printed in the United States of America ∞

WHAT DO YOU SEEK?

SESSION 1 | WHAT DO YOU SEEK?

WELCOME

Welcome to THE SEARCH. The purpose of this small group is twofold. First, to get to know one another better. Secondly, to share our reactions to the key points made in the video. Therefore, we'll start each small group with a question about ourselves. We'll try to keep our answers to two minutes or less. There is no pressure to share in this group. Just simply say "pass" if you would rather not say anything. Please feel free to express what you agree with, or what you disagree with, or what you might be struggling to understand.

GETTING TO KNOW YOU

Let's go around the group and introduce ourselves. Where do you live? How long have you lived here? Where do you work? Are you married? Do you have children? What is a hobby/activity you enjoy? Finally, why did you come to THE SEARCH?

We are going to discuss some quotes from the video. Please share your honest reaction with the group, whatever that may be. But, before we start, let's establish an important ground rule for how we engage in discussion: Seek first to understand, then to be understood. In other words, let's practice active listening and really try to understand the point of view of the person sharing, especially if we don't agree. Refrain from interrupting or correcting one another, or speaking too long when you're given the chance. Feel free to write down your thoughts, or things that were said, in the space for notes under each point. Let's begin.

"

The part we often overlook is really the most important part of a tombstone;
it's that little thing between those two dates—the dash.

CHRIS STEFANICK

Love, Family Children & Grandchildren Living A good Christian Life.

"

Happiness is "the cause of some going to war, and of others avoiding it" and it "is
the motive of every action of every man, even of those who hang themselves."[1]

CHRIS STEFANICK, QUOTING BLAISE PASCAL

We Find Happiness in Spending time with Love ones. Happiness is in Doing A good job At A job you Like.

[1] Blaise Pascal, *Pensées* 7.425, in "Morality and Doctrine," trans. W. F. Trotter (Mineola, N.Y.: Dover Publications, 2018).

SESSION 1 | WHAT DO YOU SEEK?

The findings in an eighty-year-long Harvard study suggest that happiness leads to better health and longer living, and a key predictor is found in belonging to a loving community.[2]

_____

_____

_____

_____

_____

_____

_____

According to counselor Jim Owens, many suffer from "destination addiction," the belief that happiness will not arrive until a particular circumstance changes in our lives.

_____ material Thing never cause long term happiness _____

_____

_____

_____

_____

[2] Liz Mineo, "Good Genes Are Nice, But Joy Is Better," _The Harvard Gazette_, April 11, 2017.

"

Maybe the first mission in life as an adult is to find the meaning and purpose in your life, because you will not find happiness unless you know what the meaning and purpose of life is.

JIM OWENS

_____

_____

_____

_____

_____

_____

_____

"

What if we are throwing away religion because of what we think it is?

CHRIS STEFANICK

_____

_____

_____

_____

"

What do you seek?

JESUS CHRIST, QUOTED IN JOHN 1:38

_____

_____

_____

_____

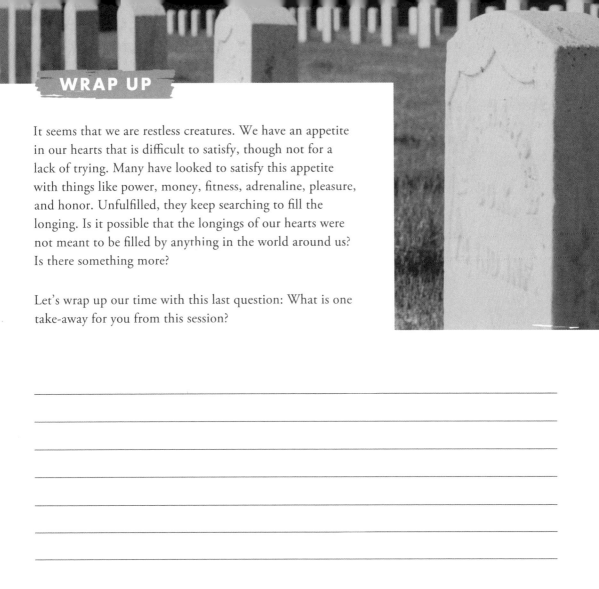

WRAP UP

It seems that we are restless creatures. We have an appetite in our hearts that is difficult to satisfy, though not for a lack of trying. Many have looked to satisfy this appetite with things like power, money, fitness, adrenaline, pleasure, and honor. Unfulfilled, they keep searching to fill the longing. Is it possible that the longings of our hearts were not meant to be filled by anything in the world around us? Is there something more?

Let's wrap up our time with this last question: What is one take-away for you from this session?

_____

_____

_____

_____

_____

_____

_____

CLOSING PRAYER

Dear God, thank you for this group. Thank you for the opportunity to wrestle with the big questions in life. May each of us come to a sense of peace about who we are and what is the purpose of our lives. Amen.

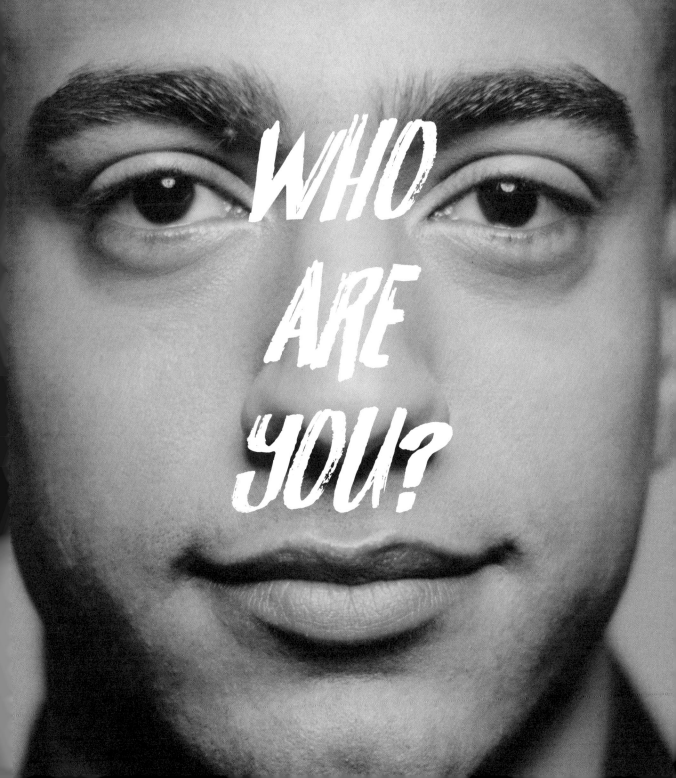

SESSION 2

WHO ARE YOU?

WELCOME BACK

Welcome back to THE SEARCH. As a reminder, the purpose of this small group is to get to know one another better and to share our thoughts about the video. Let's recap where we have been so far. In our last session, we explored our desire to be happy and how that desire can leave us searching for more than this life has to offer.

GETTING TO KNOW YOU

Let's go around the group and answer the following questions: Where did you grow up? Can you tell us a little bit about your family of origin? Can you share a memory from your childhood that you cherish? Again, let's try to keep our answers to two minutes or less.

We are going to discuss quotes from the video. Please share your honest reaction with the group, whatever that may be. Remember our ground rules for discussion: (1) seek first to understand, then to be understood; (2) refrain from interrupting or correcting one another, or speaking too long when you're given the chance. Feel free to write down in your guide your thoughts, or things that were said, in the space for notes under each point.

"

Sure, there are trillions of stars in our galaxies. There are tens of trillions of living cells in your body—each in its own way more spectacular than a lifeless star.

CHRIS STEFANICK

_____

_____

_____

_____

_____

"

You think of the other things the brain can do, the higher cognitive functions, the thinking, the intellect, the will to do something, to go beyond yourself—it has to point to something greater.

DR. PAUL CAMARATA

_____

_____

_____

_____

_____

"

Our experiences are simply inconsistent with the idea that you are just a lump of self-aware molecules that happened to emerge from primal sludge.

CHRIS STEFANICK

_____

_____

_____

_____

_____

_____

_____

"

The human person has always been trying to share this part of themselves that they don't even necessarily have the words to describe what it is. But they still had to make that sculpture; they still had to make that painting—there is something in them that was driving them to do this, to express this.

ELIZABETH ZELASKO

_____

_____

_____

_____

_____

_____

_____

"

We are rational animals. . . . That means that we can think, that we can will freely, that we can love. So, the rational part of us which makes us a particular kind of being, not just an animal, is precisely what we call the soul.

DR. SEAN INNERST

_____

_____

_____

_____

_____

_____

_____

_____

"

And one study gets even stranger. It shows that eighty percent of the people who were born blind, who have near-death experiences, come back with vivid descriptions of things they had seen.

CHRIS STEFANICK

_____

_____

_____

"

Some people say "I'm spiritual but not religious." As human beings we have a need to express these spiritual realities bodily because we are not just spirits.

CHRIS STEFANICK

_____

_____

_____

"

One hundred sixty-plus years ago, probably the majority of voting citizens in the United States said, "I had zero rights, that I was property." The fact that they said that didn't change the eternal truth that I was made in the image of God and that I am deserving of human dignity and human freedom and all the human and civil rights that come along with that.

LOUIS BROWN

_____

_____

_____

The sheer scale of the universe is hard to imagine. Current scientific estimates indicate that the universe is 93 billion light-years in diameter, growing at an increasing rate, and has existed for about 13.7 billion years. The more you contemplate the vastness of the cosmos, the smaller you might start to feel. But it's important not to confuse small with insignificant. Scientists claim that the precise age, size, and rate of expansion in the universe is what allows life to exist on this "little" planet we call earth. One could argue that we humans are so significant that the universe is bending over backwards to sustain us!

Let's wrap up our time with this last question: What is one take-away for you from this session?

_____

_____

_____

_____

_____

_____

_____

CLOSING PRAYER

Dear God, it seems implausible that our existence is random. Thank you for the gift of life. Thank you for the ability to know and to love. May each of us come to a greater understanding of our dignity and the dignity of others. Amen.

WHY A GOD?

WELCOME BACK

Welcome back to THE SEARCH. Let's recap where we have been so far. In session 1, we explored our desire to be happy and how that desire can leave us searching for more than this life has to offer. In session 2, we discussed how we are more than just matter and that we have an eternal soul.

GETTING TO KNOW YOU

Starting with the person whose birthday is closest to today, let's answer the following questions: Where did you go to high school? What extracurriculars were you involved in? Did you work in high school? Can you share a memory from your adolescence that you cherish? Again, let's try to keep our answers to two minutes or less.

We are going to continue to seek first to understand, then to be understood. Feel free to write in your guide your thoughts, or things that were said, in the space for notes under each point.

❝

We don't think that God is some mythological creature flying around in space. We believe that God is existence itself. That space and time are flying around in him.

CHRIS STEFANICK

_____

_____

_____

_____

_____

❝

Those who came long before Christianity such as the Greek philosophers came to an understanding, just through the use of reason alone, that God must exist.

JOSEPH PEARCE

_____

_____

_____

_____

_____

"

I think we are the first era in history to have so many people say, "God, if you are really there, why don't you reveal yourself to us?" I think God is looking down from Heaven saying: "Did you not notice everything?"

CHRIS STEFANICK

_____
_____
_____
_____
_____
_____
_____
_____

"

If you are doing science and you're doing it for real, then you are looking for the truth. And the Church is all about the truth.

FR. PAUL MUELLER, SJ

_____
_____
_____
_____
_____
_____
_____
_____

"

Science can tell us the "how" of things, "how" the universe works.
But it can't address certain questions about the "why" of the
universe—why was it created; why are we here?

DR. JACK WETTERER

_____

_____

_____

_____

_____

_____

_____

_____

"

Faith isn't antiscience. Faith gave birth to the sciences.

CHRIS STEFANICK

_____

_____

_____

"

When I read Genesis, I have modern cosmology in the back of my mind, and I see harmony. I think that the way I read Genesis has become more beautiful the more I learn about our cosmology, our origins, and not less so.

KARIN ÖBERG

_____

_____

_____

"

Faith is a choice. It's a reasonable choice. But let me go a step further. If you want a meaningful life, if you want joy and peace and happiness and a sense of purpose, it is also a necessary choice.

CHRIS STEFANICK

_____

_____

_____

Some people attempt to use science to discredit those who believe in God. They try to create a dichotomy between faith and science, as if the two are mutually exclusive. It may be surprising to hear that some of the leading scientists throughout history were not only people of faith, but priests. Theology has traditionally been considered a sacred science; it seeks the truth, just as science seeks verifiable facts. Ultimately, theology aims to answer questions that science cannot like: *Why is there something rather than nothing? Why is that something ordered and not chaotic? What caused that order? What is my place in the order of things?*

Let's wrap up our time with this last question: What is one take-away for you from this session?

_____

_____

_____

_____

_____

_____

_____

CLOSING PRAYER

Dear God, thank you for the ability to observe, study, and marvel at the created universe. May we be drawn to understand more deeply not only creation, but the Creator. We ask for the gift of faith. Amen.

WHAT'S OUR STORY?

SESSION 4 | WHAT'S OUR STORY?

WELCOME BACK

Welcome back to THE SEARCH. Let's recap where we have been so far. In session 1, we explored our desire to be happy and how that desire can leave us searching for more than this life has to offer. In session 2, we discussed how we are more than just matter and that we have an eternal soul. In session 3, we discussed that faith is reasonable and necessary for a sense of meaning and purpose in life.

GETTING TO KNOW YOU

Starting with the person who has traveled the farthest distance to be here, let's answer the following questions: What did you do after high school? Did you go to college or into the workforce or military? Can you share a cherished memory from your life at this time?

We are going to continue to seek first to understand, then to be understood. Feel free to write in your guide your thoughts, or things that were said, in the space for notes under each point.

"

At the heart of the Christian faith is the love of God that we see most clearly revealed to us in the Trinity. . . . God is three Persons who from all eternity love one another.

DR. MICHAEL BARBER

_____

_____

_____

_____

_____

"

An act of love is what brings us from nothingness into existence.

CHRIS STEFANICK

_____

_____

_____

_____

_____

"

The biblical story describes the Garden as a paradise. That is a beautiful
picture of what God originally intended for the human race—in communion
with each other, and with nature, and with him.

DR. SEAN INNERST

_____

_____

_____

_____

_____

_____

"

What happens with the Fall? . . . Because the most important and foundational
relationship with God is broken, all these other relationships fall apart as well.
The intellect becomes darkened; the will becomes weakened; the passions are
disordered; the relationship between Adam and Eve is broken; . . . the relationship
with creation is broken as well; . . . the world becomes broken.

DR. BEN AKERS

_____

_____

_____

_____

_____

_____

_____

"

We don't live in the world God made. We live in
the world we have made of the world God made.

DR. SEAN INNERST

_____

_____

_____

_____

_____

_____

"

The maker of space and time so loved you that he entered space and time to save you.

CHRIS STEFANICK

"

Take the love story out of the Bible . . . and what you're left with is a to-do list.

CHRIS STEFANICK

"

For a Christian, joy isn't what happens when life is going perfectly; it's what happens when you know you are loved perfectly, even when life is a mess.

CHRIS STEFANICK

We all love a good story—from the characters, the twists and turns of a captivating plot, and the dynamics of a conflict, to the resolution at the end. Perhaps we love stories because they give us insight into ourselves, animating a deeper sense of meaning in our lives. The Bible is the story of God's love for us. It begins with him creating us out of love, redeeming us by that love, and finally transforming us in his love. This divine author is love—an eternal exchange of love within the life of the Blessed Trinity: Father, Son, and Holy Spirit. What a story!

Let's wrap up our time with this last question: What is one take-away for you from this session?

_____

_____

_____

_____

_____

_____

_____

CLOSING PRAYER

Dear God, the story of salvation has been called the greatest story ever told. What makes this story great is that it impacts each of us personally in that it is our own story. Created out of love to be redeemed and transformed by love, may each of us say yes to a saving relationship with you. Amen.

SESSION 5

WHO iS JESUS?

SESSION 5 | WHO IS JESUS?

WELCOME BACK

Welcome back to THE SEARCH. Let's recap where we have been so far. In session 1, we discussed that the desires of our heart point us to something more. In session 2, we pondered the profound reality that the moment of our conception was the beginning of our eternity. In session 3, we discussed that faith is reasonable and necessary for a sense of meaning and purpose in life. Finally, in session 4, we considered that the story of the Bible is ultimately a love story about God and us.

GETTING TO KNOW YOU

Up to this point we have been sharing some details from our past. Now let's consider the future. Starting with the person who is willing to go first, let's answer the following questions: What is something you hope to accomplish in the next five years? What is one thing you hope to experience in your lifetime? Finally, is there one thing you would regret not doing before you breathe your last breath?

We are going to continue to seek first to understand, then to be understood. Feel free to write in your guide your thoughts, or things that were said, in the space for notes under each point.

"

Jesus Christ is easily the most dominant figure in all of history. That makes no sense at all. A guy that had no money, no armies, no power—the most dominant figure in all of history?

CHRIS STEFANICK

_____

_____

_____

_____

_____

"

At the center of Christianity is the claim that God came looking for us.

CHRIS STEFANICK

_____

_____

_____

_____

_____

"

We have more historical evidence about Jesus of Nazareth than we have about
most other ancient historical figures that people never call into question.

DR. BRANT PITRE

_____

_____

_____

_____

_____

_____

_____

"

These are the three options. Jesus was either a liar, or a lunatic, or he was in fact
the Lord. And you have to make your choice.

DR. BRANT PITRE

_____

_____

_____

_____

_____

_____

_____

"

There are prophecies in the Jewish Scriptures about Jesus being born in Bethlehem, his being raised in Nazareth, his going into Jerusalem riding on a donkey—prophecies even about his suffering and his death on Good Friday. . . . God was preparing humanity to understand who this man was when he would show up on the scene.

DR. EDWARD SRI

_____

_____

_____

_____

_____

_____

"

Jesus reflects a perfect humanity—not less human for being more perfect, but precisely more human for being the perfect expression of what God had willed for the human race from the beginning.

DR. SEAN INNERST

_____

_____

_____

_____

_____

_____

"

All the stuff we do as Christians is not about adding to-dos to our already overwhelmingly busy lives. The stuff we do as Christians is about drawing near to the source of life itself.

CHRIS STEFANICK

_____

_____

_____

_____

_____

_____

WRAP UP

It is without question that no person has changed the world like Jesus of Nazareth. Time is measured by his birth, churches were built to worship him in every corner of the world, cities were named after his followers, and his life has captured countless works of art and literature. Is he a legend, a liar, a lunatic? Or, is he who he claimed to be—God in the flesh? Jesus asked Simon Peter, "Who do you say that I am?" (Matthew 16:15). He asks the same question of us.

Let's wrap up our time with this last question: What is one take-away for you from this session?

_____

_____

_____

_____

_____

_____

_____

CLOSING PRAYER

Dear Jesus, in your divinity you reveal to us who God is and in your humanity you reveal to us who we are. May we have the confidence to respond like Peter to the question: Who do you say that I am? "You are the Messiah, the Son of the living God" (see Matthew 16:16). Amen.

AM i SAVED?

SESSION 6 | AM I SAVED?

WELCOME BACK

Welcome back to THE SEARCH. Let's recap where we have been so far. In session 1, we discussed that we were made for more than this life has to offer. In session 2, we discussed that we are body and soul. In session 3, we discussed that faith is both reasonable and necessary. In session 4, we discussed that the Bible is ultimately a love story about God and us. Finally, in session 5, we discussed how Jesus is both God and man and therefore reveals to us who God is and who we are.

GETTING TO KNOW YOU

We have come a long way over the past five weeks with getting to know one another. We have shared details from our past and dreams for our future. In this session, let's share where we are at right now. Starting with the person who would like to go first, let's go around the group and answer the following questions: If you had unlimited resources, how would you live your life? What important principles do you live by? What do you think is the difference between living and existing?

WHAT DO YOU THINK?

We are going to continue to seek first to understand, then to be understood. Feel free to write in your guide your thoughts, or things that were said, in the space for notes under each point.

> **"**
>
> I think for a lot of people salvation is just fire insurance. . . . But the reality is that in the New Testament, salvation isn't just about what will happen to us after we die—it very much pertains to the here and now as well. In fact, what is it that we need to be saved from: we are enslaved by sin.
>
> **DR. MICHAEL BARBER**

_____

_____

_____

_____

_____

> **"**
>
> Sin is not just a violation of a rule; it's a violation of reality. . . . Whenever we sin, we are acting not just against God . . . we are acting against our own best interests.
>
> **DR. SEAN INNERST**

_____

_____

_____

_____

_____

"

That's all the moral framework of the Church and Christianity is. . . . God is not trying to make us miserable; he is actually trying to make us thrive.

JIM BECKMAN

_____
_____
_____
_____
_____
_____
_____

"

Make no mistake about this. God is attracted to your poverty.
He actually wants to come into that mess.

JIM BECKMAN

_____
_____
_____
_____
_____
_____

"

The triumph of our faith is not that there is no suffering.
The triumph of our faith is that he has defeated it.

NOELLE GARCIA

"

Grace enables us to return to the likeness of God which Adam
and Eve lost in the very beginning.

DR. SEAN INNERST

_____

_____

_____

"

Jesus did not just come to make bad people good. He came to make dead people alive.

CHRIS STEFANICK

_____

_____

_____

"

Have you said yes to God? Love doesn't force himself on you. Love waits for your yes.

CHRIS STEFANICK

_____

_____

_____

A wealthy young man approached Jesus and asked: "What must I do to inherit eternal life?" (Mark 10:17). Like the young man, who saw salvation as a *future* event, we often want to be assured that life after death will be good. We sometimes fall into the mentality that getting to Heaven is a matter of punching a particular ticket, or checking all the boxes on a list. Jesus' first instructions almost sound like that. "Follow the commandments," he replied (see Mark 10:19). However, just as the young man thinks he has a handle on his salvation, Jesus adds, "Sell everything, give it to the poor, and follow me" (see Mark 10:21). When the young man walked away, even the disciples were surprised. They asked Jesus: "Who then can be saved?" (Mark 10:26). Jesus replied, "With man it is impossible, but not with God. For all things are possible with God" (Mark 10:27). Jesus redirects their focus from "what must I do" to "what only God can do."

Let's wrap up our time with this last question: What is one take-away for you from this session?

_____

_____

_____

_____

_____

_____

CLOSING PRAYER

Dear Jesus, it is said that you were no greater teacher than when you were hanging on the Cross, because it is there that we see a window into the very life of the Blessed Trinity—total selfless love. Thank you for making it possible for us to share in this blessed Trinitarian love. Jesus, we trust in you. Amen.

SESSION 7

WHY A CHURCH?

SESSION 7 | WHY A CHURCH?

WELCOME BACK

Welcome back to THE SEARCH. Let's recap where we have been so far. In session 1, we discussed that we were made for more than this life has to offer. In session 2, we discussed that we are body and soul. In session 3, we discussed that faith is both reasonable and necessary. In session 4, we discussed that the Bible is ultimately a love story about God and us. In session 5, we discussed how Jesus reveals to us who God is and who we are. Finally, in session 6, we discussed that salvation is a gift from God through Jesus Christ that requires our "yes."

GETTING TO KNOW YOU

Since this is our last session together, there will not be any "Getting to Know You" questions. Rather, there will be questions after we discuss the video.

WHAT DO YOU THINK?

We are going to continue to seek first to understand, then to be understood. Feel free to write in your guide your thoughts, or things that were said, in the space for notes under each point.

"

I had the great opportunity to take some pretty spectacular journeys in my life. . . . A harder journey to take is a journey of faith. It doesn't sound exciting like a space flight; but it is ultimately the most important journey we can take as human beings.

GENERAL KEVIN CHILTON

_____

_____

_____

_____

_____

"

The Church is essentially a way for us to encounter the presence of God that we need to live life to the full. It's the place where we can look for authoritative teaching, interpreting all that he left us and helping us to apply it to our lives today.

CHRIS STEFANICK

_____

_____

_____

_____

_____

"

What the research shows is that people who went through their life connected to a community . . . ended up physically and emotionally in much better shape than their peers. As a Catholic, this research is no surprise to me, that we were made by relationship for relationship.

JIM OWENS

_____
_____
_____
_____
_____
_____

"

The fact that God saves us as a family means . . . that we have an organized religion. Religion was never meant to be a private, personal thing.

CHRIS STEFANICK

_____
_____
_____
_____
_____
_____

"

We have bodies; we exist in these bodies, and so the spiritual life of the person also has to include the body. The liturgical experience is part of that.

JONATHAN PAGEAU

"

[In the sacraments,] we literally get God's life to begin the process of change and transformation to become, not just who we are, but who we were created to be—who we are destined to be.

JIM BECKMAN

_____

_____

_____

"

Taking the Eucharist to orbit for me was a big deal. And receiving the Eucharist on Sunday for me is a big deal because I believe it is what Jesus says it is.

GENERAL KEVIN CHILTON

_____

_____

_____

"

A lot of people say, "I don't want to follow some man-made religion." You know what, I don't either. Our religion was founded by Jesus Christ.

CHRIS STEFANICK

_____

_____

_____

St. Augustine, in reference to Holy Communion, wrote: "Be what you can see, and receive what you are."[3] Jesus didn't simply leave us a message or instructions to follow. He left us a living, dynamic Church where we could continue to encounter him and be transformed into his likeness.

We have concluded THE SEARCH. Starting with the person who would like to go first, please share with the group what this seven-week experience has meant to you.

[Optional if there is time] Let's go around the circle one last time. However, instead of answering a question, let's focus on each person for a minute and share things we remember them saying over the course of these seven weeks. For example, you might say: "I remember you saying that a cherished memory from your childhood was [fill in the blank]."

_____

_____

_____

_____

_____

_____

CLOSING PRAYER

Heavenly Father, you have made us to be in communion with you and with one another. Thank you for the blessing of those who know, love, and care for us. Lord Jesus, thank you for the gift of the Church and the part it plays in your plan for humanity. Forgive us for the times we fail to be the people you desire us to be. Holy Spirit, thank you for dwelling within us and for the gifts you give us to build up the Church. Help us to produce the fruits of your love more abundantly in our lives. **All:** Glory be to the Father, and to the Son, and to the Holy Spirit. As it was in the beginning, is now, and ever shall be, world without end. Amen.

[3] St. Augustine, Sermon 272, in _Essential Sermons_, trans. Edmund Hill, O.P. (Hyde Park, N.Y.: New City Press, 2007), p. 318.

NOTES

THE
SEARCH
CONTINUES

We hope you've enjoyed *The Search!*

Going through *The Search* likely brought up more questions. Is there right and wrong? Where did the Bible come from? Why is there a pope? What is the Mass?

Based on the top internet searches on Faith and God, Chris Stefanick sits down with today's leading theologians to answer these questions and more in *The Search Continues*. Each short conversational episode answers questions about the Faith, in a practical and easy-to-understand format.

Continue your search at
watch.formed.org/the-search-continues

FORMED®
THE CATHOLIC FAITH.
ON DEMAND.

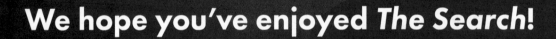

Interested in starting your own Search group? Get the materials you need at **Catholic.Market/the-search/**